MY POSTPARTUM SELF CARE, SUPPORT AND EMOTIONAL WELLNESS PLAN

THIS PLAN BELONGS TO:

....

I WILL SHARE MY PLAN WITH:

....

lifewithbabyworkbook.com

ISBN: 978-1-7338809-0-9

This is a workbook. A guide. A plan.

No matter how you enter parenthood, whether through giving birth, adopting, or blending families, it is a transition. And with all transitions, there are ups and downs and adjustments.

This workbook was created to help prepare mothers (and their support person) to feel empowered during pregnancy, through the postpartum period. Every parent deserves to feel peace and happiness. Emotional health and wellness is critical during this exciting, but vulnerable time.

Why was this workbook created?

- Women and families experience so many similar challenges and emotions after having a baby, yet it's often difficult to talk about them. Our society does not do a good job at creating a safe place for these challenges to be talked about openly. Many families feel alone, as if they are the only ones facing hardship.
- The more we talk about these issues during the postpartum time, the more connected and less alone everyone can feel.
- Parenthood should not feel like suffering.
- Information and concrete tools identified within this postpartum workbook will help create a healthy postpartum transition time, and build a strong foundation to take care of yourself through all of parenthood.

Why is having a postpartum emotional health plan so important?

- Postpartum depression is the #1 complication from childbirth. It's important to educate and empower mothers and their support people to know how to handle any Postpartum Mood and Anxiety Disorder, if one should arise.

- Some women have never experienced any mental health issues and may feel blindsided should symptoms appear during the postpartum period. This plan helps to navigate this time and provides a framework for these experiences.

- Talking openly about the reality of postpartum emotions helps fight the stigma associated with mental health. This is critical for saving and improving mothers' lives.

This Postpartum Workbook Focuses On:

- **Section 1** - Everyday basics of life that are often overlooked during the postpartum period including self care, building a support network, sleep, and nutrition. Each of these four parts include facts and tips on how to support yourself as well as guidelines for when more support may be needed.
- **Section 2** - A postpartum emotional wellness plan for the mother's partner/spouse/support person.
- **Section 3** - Emotional health including risk factors for developing a Postpartum Mood and Anxiety Disorder, symptoms, action steps and resources to find relief.
- **Section 4** - Practical tools you can use to help prioritize what needs to get done and nurture yourself along the way.

It's important to note that for the purposes of this workbook, depression and anxiety are discussed in the postpartum period. However, depression and anxiety can also happen during pregnancy. If you are pregnant and have concerns about depression or anxiety, reach out to your provider.

How to Use this Workbook

- This workbook is for you! The more you put into it, the more you will get out of it.
- Take as much time as you need to fill out each section, and be as thorough as possible.
- Ideally this workbook would be completed during pregnancy, in collaboration with your support person and providers. However, it can be used at any point, even after baby arrives.
- It is designed to have you think about yourself and generate conversations around your specific needs with your support people.
- Share and talk about your plan. Support people want to help, but often do not know how. Give them the information they need to help support you during this time of transition.
- Some of the pages within this workbook are meant to be completed and cut out to share. They will have the ✂ icon.
- You may want to have a highlighter or pen readily available while reading this workbook. There's a lot of good information and indicating parts that stand out to you will help you find them more quickly.
- Throughout this workbook, the phrase "reach out for more help" is used. This phrase is meant to have you connect with your providers for more support. You will complete a list of providers on your team on page 15.

It is important to recognize that every mom and family is unique. This workbook will help you focus on the basics needed during your postpartum period, but it is not comprehensive in addressing all issues that may arise. It also helps to provide education around supporting your emotional wellness though it is not meant to replace treatment. When in doubt, seek additional support, and ask for help when needed.

The journey of parenthood is an opportunity to grow and deepen your relationships. Trust your instincts, and enjoy the journey!

TABLE OF CONTENTS

SELF CARE

It's easy to lose sight of your own needs after your baby is born.

Remember, taking care of yourself makes you more available to care for your baby's needs. Self care is not indulgent nor does it have to be luxurious. A few minutes of intentional time, just for you, can replenish your body and mind.

GOOD TO KNOW

- ✓ Self care does not have to require a lot of time. You may think you don't have time for it, but taking 5-15 minutes to yourself, throughout the day, can make a difference.
- ✓ It's common for mothers to feel "touched out." This means your nervous system is overloaded from the constant physical demands of feeding and caring for your infant (plus from other children you may have in the home as well). Sit alone for 5 minutes to take a break from touch, noise, and light as needed.
- ✓ Self care looks different for everyone. Try to not compare yourself to other moms.
- ✓ Self care is showing compassion for yourself.
- ✓ It's ok to take a break from social media if it makes you feel judged, anxious or isolated.
- ✓ This is one of the most demanding adjustments of your life! Take your time, and celebrate the small victories. Every feeding, diaper change, snuggle is tremendous.
- ✓ Think of everything in terms of "for right now." This means to remember this phase is temporary. The goal is to make it day to day until you find your family's new rhythm. For example, say, "for right now, it's ok the dishes aren't done." Or, "for right now, it's ok to let the baby fall asleep in my arms vs. in the crib."
- ✓ No one has this all figured out!

SELF CARE

SELF CARE TIPS

1 You may find that you are struggling with giving yourself "permission" to take care of you. Think of you and your baby like a system, from birth to a year postpartum. Caring for one part of the system is caring for the other.

2 Try to recognize and ignore expectations around what your baby will be like and how you will mother. Invite flexibility and curiosity as you get to know your baby and yourself as a new mother.

3 Remember, every baby is different and every mom is different. Try not to compare yourself to family members, friends, social media, or even other babies you've had. Your experience is valid and unique.

4 Post reminder signs about self care around your home, in places you will see often. See page 70 for prompt cards you can use. Practice self compassion. Talk to yourself like you would talk to your best friend.

5 When you feel overwhelmed or anxious, try to shift your attention to what is working. "My heart is beating." "My baby is growing." "I am learning." See page 50 for more tips.

6 Sex can be tricky both physically and emotionally after baby arrives. You and your partner may have different expectations; your body has changed, and you will both be exhausted. The key is communication. Talk about how you are both feeling emotionally. Talk about how your body is feeling. Talk about different ways, other than sex, to define intimacy in your relationship. There are other forms of touch that allow for affection and connection. And when you're both ready for sex, it's recommended to use lubrication and go slow.

7 Physical discomfort/pain after childbirth can elevate emotions, especially anxiety. This includes any part of your body, especially your breasts, nipples, vaginal area and/or c-section scar.

* WHEN TO REACH OUT FOR MORE SUPPORT *

- If you have used your self care tips and they do not provide you with any relief.
- If your mood is low and/or anxiety is high even after incorporating self care.

MY SELF CARE PLAN

1. WHAT ARE THINGS I CAN DO FOR 5, 10, OR 15 MINUTES THAT MAKE ME FEEL GOOD?

Example: Taking a hot shower, listening to music, journaling, meditating, going for a short walk.

2. HOW DO I KNOW WHEN I NEED TO USE MY SELF CARE IDEAS?

Example: Notice shallow breathing, holding breath, tight shoulders, irritability, feelings of being overwhelmed.

SELF CARE IDEAS

- Close your eyes, take a few deep breaths.
- Checking in with yourself– are you hungry, thirsty, need to go to the bathroom?
- Take a shower or bath.
- Listen to music or watch a funny movie.
- Light a candle and enjoy the smell.
- Don't forget to eat! Snack often and stay hydrated.
- Pray or meditate.
- Nap when you can.
- Take a walk outside – with your baby or leave baby with a support person.
- Journal, write down your thoughts.
- Post affirmations around your house. See page 67 for more affirmations.
  - The decisions made by other moms don't need to influence mine.
  - Not loving every moment of motherhood doesn't mean anything about my love for my kid(s).
  - I am learning how to be a mother.
- Connect with nature - walk outside, look at the sky, sit in the sun.
- Accept help when offered. Ask for help when needed.

SUPPORT NETWORK

The goal of your support network is to help decrease your stress and provide comfort.

There are different types of support including practical, emotional, and financial. Think about the people who make up your village. What would be helpful for them to do, or NOT do? Remember, often times people feel good when they can help. They just need to know what to do. Let them help!

Remember

YOU ARE NOT ALONE

GOOD TO KNOW

- ✓ Support during the postpartum period includes help from people around you including friends, family, community groups, and professionals.
- ✓ You may have the urge to look online for questions you have about you or your baby. While the Internet can provide a lot of good information, it can also be overwhelming and create new worries. Consider asking your support person to look up your questions and identify the most important information. This helps prevent you falling into the worry spiral of the Internet. You can also choose to not look up anything online and call or message your provider directly with questions.
- ✓ Parenthood can feel very isolating, even when you are surrounded by people. It's important to connect with people that understand your situation, and can relate to your feelings.
- ✓ Ask your provider(s) for any recommendations on ways to connect with other moms and families that are in similar stages of parenthood.
- ✓ It's helpful to identify your support network while you are still pregnant, but it can be done after baby arrives as well.
- ✓ Community support groups are a great way to meet other parents. Many groups are held through hospitals, birthing centers, doula groups, lactation groups, etc. Search for local options in your area or contact Postpartum Support International (PSI) for local resources at 1-800-944-4773 or postpartum.net.
- ✓ Online support groups are helpful to connect with other parents without leaving your home. This can be comforting during the middle of the night when feelings of loneliness tend to rise.
- ✓ Professional providers work best when they all talk. Ask your provider if you can sign a release of information for other providers involved in your care. Then ask each provider to collaborate with one another.
- ✓ It can be hard to ask for help. If you find yourself having a hard time saying out loud what you need, try writing it down.
- ✓ Remember, asking for help is not a sign of weakness. It is one of the bravest actions you can take.

GOOD TO KNOW

Below are common thoughts moms may experience during the postpartum period. While they can be difficult to fully understand, remember they are rooted in the discomfort that occurs during a time of transition. It's ok to allow yourself the time and space to feel any emotion that may arise.

- ✓ **I made a huge mistake. I cannot take care of my baby.** It is natural to feel this way; and whether or not women talk about these thoughts, many have them. Everything that you counted on before baby, that provided a sense of normalcy and support like sleep, friendships, routine, has changed. And then add in the changes of hormones, sleep deprivation and any other complications like breastfeeding challenges or a traumatic birth, all of which intensify the situation. These thoughts can lead to serious feelings of guilt. Be kind and gentle to yourself. Try not to judge the thoughts you are having. You are in transition and transition invites upheaval. And most importantly, know these thoughts are in no way an indication of what kind of mom you are or how much you love your baby.

- ✓ **I cannot stand my partner. I'm doing SO much more work.** In many ways you are doing more. The physical impact from pregnancy and childbirth is significant, and often difficult for someone else to fully understand. Talk with your partner. Usually these resentments are rooted in feelings of being overwhelmed and/or underappreciated. Often times small changes to schedules or tasks can help you feel more supported. Let your partner know you need to feel more recognized for your work. Remember, you have to talk to your partner about how you're feeling, or change will not happen.

- ✓ **I feel so incompetent. I don't know what my baby needs.** Many moms feel they should know what baby needs at all times. When baby continues to cry or be upset, it can cause feelings of failure and guilt. You are usually able to see the problem, think of solutions and get it fixed. But babies don't work that way. Give yourself a lot of compassion. Try not to compare your "new" self as a mom to your "old" self, pre-baby. Invite flexibility and kindness to yourself rather than judgment.

GOOD TO KNOW

✓ **I am worried I'm not loving my baby enough.** Concerns about loving your new baby can show up in different ways in the postpartum period. From worries about not falling "madly in love" with baby after delivery to "not having enough love" for second or subsequent babies, it can be stressful. These are common feelings during big transitions. Remember, these feelings are not about your parenting or love for your baby. It's a way for your brain to slowly warm up to this transition.

✓ **I really miss the old me.** Having a baby is a huge shift in your identity. It's common to feel a bit lost in it all. There will be times when you're reminded of the "old you" and times when you are facing situations that feel new and foreign. Expect to grieve your identity before pregnancy. Provide yourself space and time to acknowledge your grief as well as celebration for your joys. You are growing, transitioning and honoring your entire journey.

✓ **Remember, you can hold more than one emotion at a time.** And they can even be opposite emotions.

- You can feel tremendous love for your baby and strong anger because baby won't stop crying.
- You can feel very connected to your partner and have resentment, too.
- You can feel guilty for getting out of the house, even as the baby is crying, and joy for having some free time.

✓ **Allow yourself to feel your feelings.** Let them be. We get ourselves in trouble when we ignore, or even judge ourselves for having them. They are all valid. If you notice these difficult feelings becoming more regular (when you are having them for the majority of the day), or they become so big you have a hard time functioning, then you should let someone know and reach out for help. These could be signs that deserve a professional's opinion about next steps.

SUPPORT NETWORK

SUPPORT NETWORK TIPS

1. It's ok to ask for and receive help. You may feel like you need to do it all, but now is the time to be kind to yourself and accept help when offered. Remember, people want to help.

2. It's also ok to ask people to leave. You may have scheduled a visit, but maybe you and your baby didn't sleep well the night before. It is ok to reschedule a visit or ask someone to leave if needed. It's also ok to be clear that a meal drop is just that– not a visit.

3. Avoid spending time with people who make you anxious or overwhelmed. Again, it's ok to say no!

4. Consider registering for a birth, overnight or postpartum doula fund for your baby shower instead of traditional gifts. Example: babylist.com allows you to register for items and services from any store or website.

5. You may be well experienced in receiving advice during your pregnancy; it doesn't always stop after your baby is born. Remember, take what you like or need, and leave the rest behind. Do what works best for you and your family.

6. Connect with other moms that are going through the same experience. Meet in person, attend a moms' group, or connect online. Women need each other during this time for reassurance and support.

MY PROFESSIONAL SUPPORT NETWORK

This list is meant to be shared with your support person. Consider posting in a visible area, like your fridge, or in a place both of you can easily find.

WHO IS IN MY PROFESSIONAL SUPPORT NETWORK?	CONTACT INFO: INCLUDE NAME, PHONE NUMBER, EMAIL, PATIENT PORTAL INFO (IF APPLICABLE), AND AFTER HOURS INFO
PRIMARY PROVIDERS	
OBGYN or Midwife:	
Pediatrician:	
Primary Care Physician:	
OTHER TEAM MEMBERS (unique to each woman's needs)	
Psychiatrist or Therapist:	
Birth Doula:	
Postpartum Doula:	
Overnight Sleep Doula:	
Placenta Encapsulator:	
Lactation Consultant:	
Other: (Example: Support Group, Chiropractor, etc.)	

MY PROFESSIONAL SUPPORT NETWORK

Cut this page out and place on your fridge, or any visible area in your home.

MY SUPPORT NETWORK

WHO MAKES UP MY SUPPORT NETWORK? LIST THEM BELOW. (Example: Family, friends, community support groups, etc.)	**WHAT CAN I ASK THEM TO HELP WITH?** (Example: Take the dog for a walk, do laundry, prepare a meal, go grocery shopping, come over and spend time with me, watch the baby so I can shower, go for a walk, take a nap, etc.)

MY SUPPORT NETWORK PLAN

1. WILL I RETURN TO WORK AFTER BABY? YES NO MAYBE
IF SO, WHEN WILL I RETURN TO WORK? ....

....

2. WILL MY PARTNER/SUPPORT PERSON RETURN TO WORK AFTER BABY?
YES NO MAYBE **IF SO, WHEN WILL THIS HAPPEN?** ....

....

3. HOW CAN WE PREPARE FOR THE RETURN TO WORK? ....

....

....

Tips for Partner Returning to Work

- Work part-time or from home initially (if job allows).
- Create a visual weekly or monthly calendar to share work times, appointments, etc. (Example: Google calendar, whiteboard, traditional calendar on fridge).
- For the stay at home person, have a postpartum doula help at home during this transition. Also find people to connect with during the day.
- Clearly communicate with each other; do not assume the other person knows what is on your mind.
- Call or text to check in during the day.
- Call or text if leaving work late or plans change.
- It can be a difficult transition being at work all day and then coming home. Allowing transition space from work mode to baby/home mode will be helpful. Listen to your favorite music or podcast during your commute home, or simply enjoy silence. Consider taking public transportation to tune out after work. Spend 5 minutes of quiet time by yourself before you go inside your home.
- Honor that you will be straddling two worlds between work and baby. Both of these worlds have different demands and expectations. Remember, this is all new, so accept help when offered and give yourself breaks.

Tips for Mom Returning to Work

- Give yourself grace and compassion during this time of transition.
- Explore and confirm plans for childcare.
- Practice your new schedule - for 2 weeks prior to returning to work, wake up and go to bed at the time you need for your work schedule. This includes childcare plans. If you are using a daycare, visit the center a few times with baby to get a little more familiar with the new setting. If you are using a nanny or other in home childcare provider, have that person come over a few times to increase comfort.
- Have other people practice feeding the baby with a bottle, especially if you're breastfeeding.
- If you plan on pumping milk at work, get to know your pump, how it works and how to store breastmilk. Also talk to your employer about where you will be able to safely and privately pump and store milk at work.
- A lactation consultant can be a great resource for helping your baby take a bottle and/or understanding your pump.
- Talk to your employer about work expectations, schedules, and any flexibility during the transition back to work.
- Take care of yourself! There are often a lot of emotions around the return to work, and being away from your baby. Take it slow!

MY SUPPORT NETWORK PLAN

HOW YOUR SUPPORT NETWORK CAN HELP

Sometimes your support person will notice you aren't feeling well or acting like yourself, even before you do.

1. WHAT ARE SOME OF MY WARNING SIGNS MY SUPPORT PERSON CAN LOOK FOR?
Example: Wanting to be alone, irritability, crying easily, not wanting to care for my baby, not sleeping or sleeping too much.

MY PERSONAL WARNING SIGNS INCLUDE: ....

....

....

....

....

2. WHAT IS THE BEST WAY FOR MY SUPPORT PERSON TO CHECK IN WITH ME?
Example: Giving me a hug or back massage, taking the baby so I can have a break, providing me some time alone, reassuring me that things will be ok, calling a professional support person or provider for me, etc.

IF I NEED HELP, I WANT MY SUPPORT PERSON TO: ....

....

....

....

....

** WHEN TO REACH OUT FOR MORE SUPPORT **

- If you're still experiencing some warning signs after your support person has checked in with you, contact someone on your professional support team.

SLEEP

While it's common for parents to know that their sleep schedule will change once baby arrives, it's another experience entirely to live through it.

Lack of sleep is closely tied to changes in mood. During this time it is important to find ways to rest your body and nervous system, even if you are not able to get the full amount of sleep desired. You cannot control how often your baby will be awake, but you can plan for ways to help support your sleep.

GOOD TO KNOW

- ✓ Sleep should be one of your priorities.
- ✓ Lack of sleep is temporary. It will get better!
- ✓ Your infant will sleep in spurts; that means you will sleep in spurts too. This is a time-limited phase of development but so important to plan for so you can get as much rest as possible in between times of wakefulness.
- ✓ Every baby is different; therefore sleep is unpredictable. A baby does not know the difference between day and night. It is helpful to embrace this shift in sleep, rather than resist it.
- ✓ If you are not able to fully fall asleep, simply laying down to rest your mind and body will help relax your nervous system. Go to your quiet place (that is not your bed) and practice being still.
- ✓ If you are tracking baby's sleep cycles, find a balance. Information can be helpful to see patterns and trends but can also fuel anxiety if overdone. Notice if tracking sleep is making you more anxious or providing helpful data.
- ✓ Be flexible about sleeping arrangements. There are many options for where a baby can sleep. Do your research, talk with your baby's doctor, and choose a safe sleeping place for your baby that supports both you and your baby's sleep. Remember that newborns cannot establish any bad sleeping habits, so what you do now to maximize sleep will not have any negative impact on how your child will be sleeping when he/she is older.

SLEEP TIPS

1 You've probably heard, "sleep when the baby sleeps." This is good advice but not always doable. You may feel pressure to get things done. Invite balance—consider doing a task during one of the baby's nap, then resting during another one.

2 Exercise helps with sleep but avoid exercising two hours before bedtime.

3 Consider using an overnight doula or family/friend for nighttime support, even if just for one night per week.

4 Avoid caffeine and alcohol 6 hours before bedtime.

5 Avoid screens before bedtime - your phone, computer, TV, or iPad.

6 Do not look at your clock! If possible, turn your clock towards the wall.

7 If you cannot sleep after 20 minutes, go to a quiet, comfortable place and do something relaxing like reading.

8 Protect your space–your bed should be used for sleep and sex only.

9 If you cannot sleep because your mind is racing, write down your thoughts. Move them from your brain to paper. This can decrease the tension and energy from these thoughts.

10 Listen to a guided meditation or relaxing ambient music using headphones. Insight Timer and Calm are two wonderful free apps with many choices.

MY SLEEP PLAN

1. IDEALLY, HOW MANY HOURS DO I NEED TO SLEEP IN ORDER TO FEEL RESTED?

2. WHERE WILL MY BABY SLEEP?

3. WHAT ARE MY OVERNIGHT FEEDING PLANS? CAN A SUPPORT PERSON HELP?

4. CAN MY PARTNER AND I TAKE FEEDING SHIFTS? IS THERE ANOTHER PLACE I CAN SLEEP WHEN I AM "OFF SHIFT"?

5. WHAT CAN I PREPARE AHEAD OF TIME FOR OVERNIGHT FEEDINGS?
Example: Bottles (formula or expressed milk), bottle warmer, pumping equipment, etc.

MY SLEEP PLAN

6. WHAT IS/CAN BE MY BEDTIME RITUAL? Example: Warm bath, soaking feet, decaffeinated tea, meditation, progressive muscle relaxation, lighting incense, reading, etc.

....

....

....

....

7. FIND A QUIET, COMFORTABLE PLACE IN MY HOME WHERE I CAN GO IF I CAN'T FALL BACK ASLEEP. WHERE IS THIS PLACE FOR ME?

....

....

....

....

* *WHEN TO REACH OUT FOR MORE SUPPORT* *

- If you notice that you cannot fall asleep because of racing or overwhelming thoughts – this includes sleep around bedtime and naps.
- If you notice that you aren't tired or have extra energy even when you haven't been sleeping well.
- If you have not slept at all in 48 hours or more.
- If you notice extreme irritability or rage.
- If you notice that you are sleeping a lot and having a hard time functioning. This could mean that you don't feel like you have energy to brush your teeth, shower, do basic tasks, care for your baby, etc.

You need to fuel your body during this demanding time.

After childbirth, your body will work extremely hard to heal and recover. And if you are breastfeeding, your body will work constantly to produce milk. Even if you didn't birth your baby, you have added stress on your body. Eating the right foods, consuming enough calories, and drinking water to keep you hydrated will help give you more energy and regulate your mood.

GOOD TO KNOW

✓ Low blood sugar and dehydration can affect your mood. Check in with yourself often. Are you hungry or thirsty?

✓ If you're breastfeeding, you'll find it can make you ravenous! Try to stay on top of your meals. Your body is working extra hard to produce milk.

✓ People will want to help you after your baby arrives! Having friends/family bring food is a wonderful way to allow people to help and relieve the burden of preparing food. Create a meal calendar on mealtrain.com where people can sign up to drop off food on designated days.

FEEDING BABY

- Ensuring baby is properly fed is one of the most challenging aspects of the postpartum period. There are so many opinions and so much information that can make this process overwhelming. Some women know from the beginning they will use formula, while others hope to breastfeed, or feed baby using a combination of both. No matter how you end up feeding your baby, it is important to do what is best for your family.

- Breastfeeding issues are unique to each mom and baby. For some women it happens easily, and for others it can be a struggle. Give yourself compassion during this time, and know that if you have difficulty breastfeeding you are not broken. Consult the professionals, do your research and make the decision that is best for the entire family, not just the baby. This means accounting for your wellbeing too.

- Your worth as a mother is not defined by how much milk you produce.

- Extend respect for other families' choices around baby feeding. Everyone is different.

- It can be very helpful to get guidance from a Lactation Consultant to help support your questions regarding breast and/or bottle feeding and pumping. Ask to see a Lactation Consultant if you give birth in a hospital, or search for local resources in your community once you are home.

- Remember, as you transition away from breastfeeding, you may experience grief. Some women don't have a choice and have to stop breastfeeding before they are ready, and others decide on their own when it is time to wean. These are both transitions that require time to honor and grieve the transition from no longer breastfeeding your baby.

NUTRITION TIPS

1. Keep taking your prenatal vitamins.
2. Have easy access to snacks you can eat with one hand. Example: nuts, apples, lunch meat, etc.
3. When support people are bringing over food, it's ok to let them know it's not a time to stay and visit. They can drop off the food and schedule another time to visit with you and the baby.
4. Little sips of water and small snacks are ok in a pinch or if you don't have a strong appetite.
5. Drinking a lot of water can be hard. Think about how you can add variety like: adding lemon/lime, other fruit infusions, using a straw, having a support person bring you water, extra ice, keeping a pitcher next to you for easy refills, etc.

* WHEN TO REACH OUT FOR MORE SUPPORT *

- If you don't want to eat or if you are overeating and have significant weight loss or gain for more than two weeks.

MY NUTRITION PLAN

1. WHAT ARE SOME OF MY FAVORITE, HEALTHY FOODS I CAN MAKE AND FREEZE BEFORE BABY COMES?

2. IF PEOPLE OFFER TO BRING FOOD, DO I WANT HOME-COOKED MEALS OR SOMETHING PICKED UP FROM A RESTAURANT? REMEMBER TO INCLUDE ANY DIETARY RESTRICTIONS FOR ALL FAMILY MEMBERS.

3. IT IS REALLY IMPORTANT TO NOT SKIP MEALS, BUT IT'S EASY TO FORGET TO EAT. WHAT ARE SOME OF MY FAVORITE, EASY TO PREPARE MEALS? (EXAMPLE: CROCKPOT, SANDWICHES, WRAPS)

4. HYDRATION IS IMPORTANT. HOW CAN I REMEMBER TO DRINK ENOUGH WATER?

NUTRITION

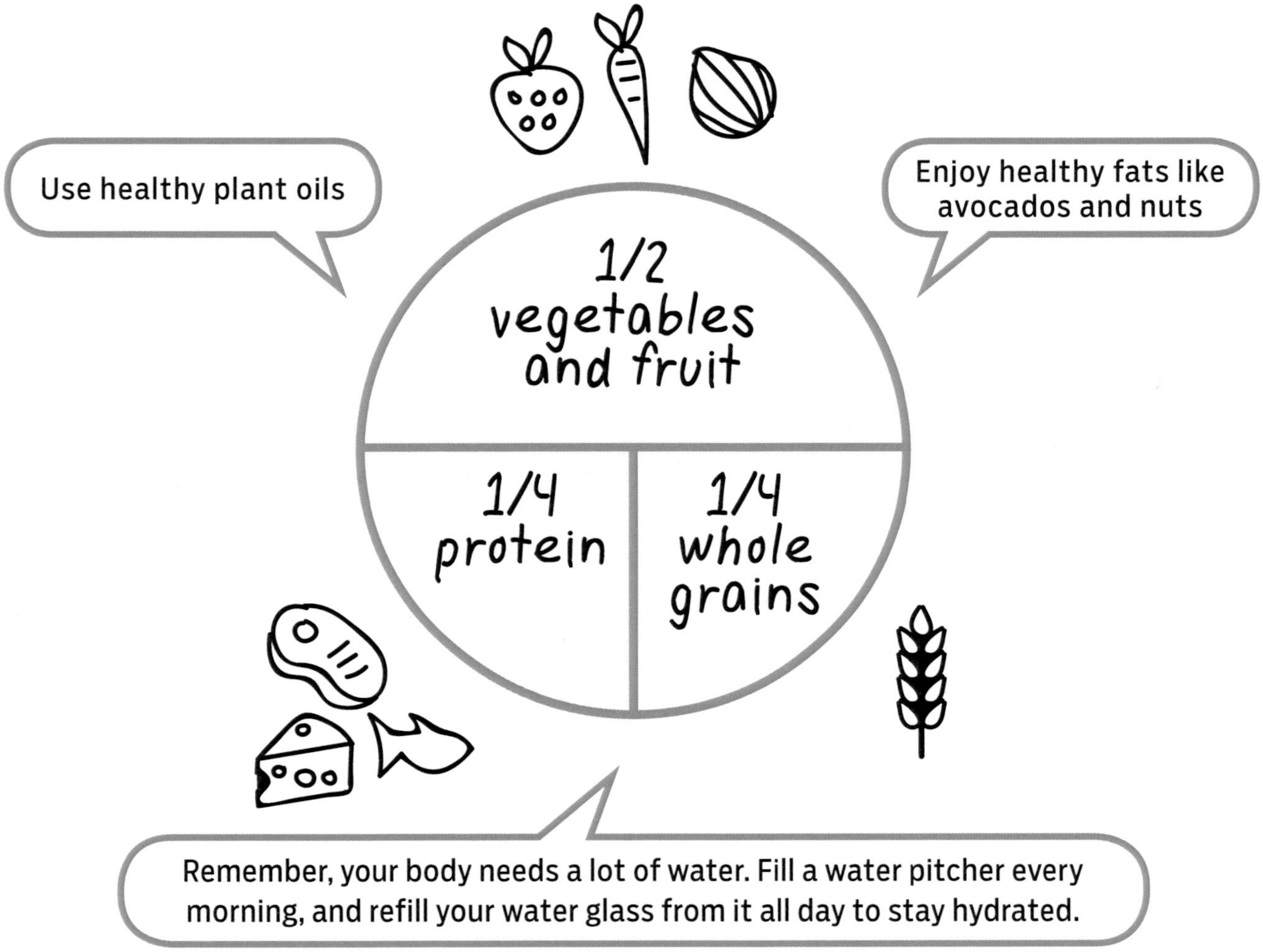
Use healthy plant oils
Enjoy healthy fats like avocados and nuts
1/2 vegetables and fruit
1/4 protein
1/4 whole grains
Remember, your body needs a lot of water. Fill a water pitcher every morning, and refill your water glass from it all day to stay hydrated.

PARTNER PLAN

It is very important to ensure the mother's support person is cared for as well during the postpartum period.

Often the needs of the support person are unintentionally delayed or overlooked because of the time and attention required for the baby and mother. Identifying and planning for the needs of the support person will help create a smoother transition, making sure everyone's needs are met.

MY PARTNER PLAN

THIS SECTION IS TO BE COMPLETED BY THE MOTHER'S PARTNER/SPOUSE/SUPPORT PERSON. IT CAN BE LEFT IN THIS WORKBOOK OR CUT OUT AND POSTED.

THIS PLAN BELONGS TO: ....

I WILL SHARE MY PLAN WITH: ....

SELF CARE

1. WHAT ARE THINGS I CAN DO FOR 5, 10, or 15 MINUTES THAT MAKE ME FEEL GOOD?

Example: Taking a hot shower, meditating, going on a short walk or quick jog..............................

....

....

....

2. HOW DO I KNOW WHEN I NEED TO USE MY SELF CARE IDEAS? Example: Notice shallow breathing, tight shoulders, irritability, feelings of being overwhelmed, etc...............................

....

....

....

SUPPORT

1. WHO MAKES UP MY SUPPORT NETWORK? Example: Family, friends, community support groups..............................

....

....

2. WHO IS MY PROFESSIONAL NETWORK? Example: Primary Care Physician, Therapist, etc...............................

....

....

3. WHAT ARE MY PERSONAL WARNING SIGNS THAT I AM FEELING DOWN, OVERWHELMED, OR IRRITABLE? Example: Isolating myself from others, changes in sleep, crying easily.

My personal warning signs include:..............................

....

....

....

MY PARTNER PLAN

4. WHAT IS THE BEST WAY FOR MY SUPPORT PERSON TO CHECK IN WITH ME? Example: Giving me a hug or back massage, providing me some time alone, reassuring me things will be ok, calling a professional support person, etc. **I want my support person to:**

SLEEP

1. IDEALLY, HOW MANY HOURS DO I NEED TO SLEEP TO FEEL RESTED?

2. WHAT IS/CAN BE MY BEDTIME RITUAL? Example: Warm bath, decaffeinated tea, meditation, progressive muscle relaxation, lighting incense, reading, etc.

NUTRITION

1. WHAT ARE SOME QUICK MEALS I ENJOY?

2. HOW DO I MAKE SURE I AM EATING ENOUGH?

SEE PAGES 36 AND 38 FOR MORE SYMPTOMS LIKE ANXIETY AND DEPRESSION THAT CAN APPEAR IN PARTNERS (INCLUDING SAME-SEX AND NON-BIOLOGICAL PARTNERS) DURING THIS TIME.

POSTPARTUM EMOTIONS

The wave of emotions experienced during the postpartum period will vary in frequency and intensity.

While some of these emotions are expected, like the Baby Blues, others can be more difficult to navigate. You may not be able to understand or even describe what you are feeling, especially with difficult emotions. This is ok. Tuning into yourself and reviewing your plan can help you understand your experience, and get connected to care more quickly. Remember, emotions are like waves in the ocean - they consistently come and go without your control, and every wave that goes up, comes back down again.

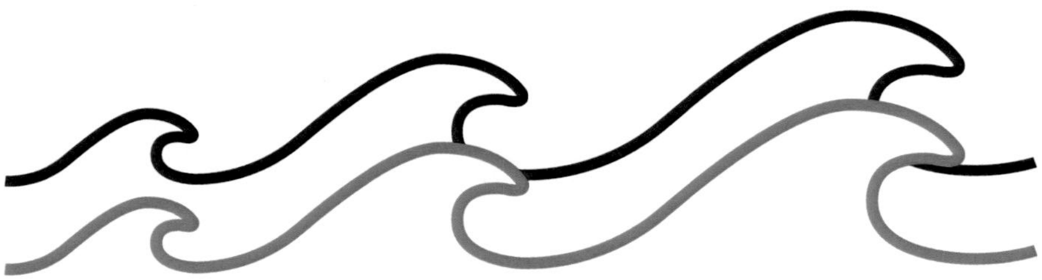

BABY BLUES

BABY BLUES REFER TO THE TYPICAL CHANGES IN MOOD AFTER YOU BABY IS BORN. On average, these feelings become more intense 4-5 days postpartum. Baby Blues are thought to be related to changes in hormones and sleep deprivation after your delivery. These feelings often get better on their own.

Baby Blues are NOT considered a mental health issue.

Up to

80%

of women experience Baby Blues in the first weeks after delivery.*

BABY BLUES
YOU MAY NOTICE SOME OF THE FOLLOWING:

- Sadness
- Feeling more sensitive
- Crying easily
- Having a hard time sleeping
- Irritability
- Feeling overwhelmed
- Not being able to explain your feelings

TO TRACK YOUR BABY BLUES WINDOW, COMPLETE THE FOLLOWING:

My delivery date: ....

Two weeks after delivery date: ....

Women can also experience feelings similar to Baby Blues during other significant hormonal shifts like the weaning process (stopping breastfeeding) and when menstruation returns.

Remember, your body and feelings during the Baby Blues window is not perfectly tied to 2 weeks. This is just an average. However, if you notice you've been experiencing the feelings listed above and they've lasted LONGER than 2 weeks since giving birth, contact your doctor, therapist or support person for help. And if you notice these feelings and they are making daily tasks more difficult or impossible, don't wait for 2 weeks to pass, reach out for help now.

*Source: National Institute of Mental Health

POSTPARTUM MOOD AND ANXIETY DISORDERS (PMADs)

POSTPARTUM MOOD AND ANXIETY DISORDERS DO NOT HAVE TO BE SCARY. EDUCATION IS POWER! It is important to talk about them, become familiar about what they are, and what to do if you experience any symptoms. Being aware of PMADs and having a plan in place provides a sense of control and security. Think of any other complication that can occur in pregnancy and/or postpartum period. Doctors have ways to recognize, treat and monitor complications to make sure it does not escalate into a larger issue. Having a PMAD is not unlike any other complication during this time. There are steps you can take to find relief.

Postpartum Mood and Anxiety Disorders include

- Anxiety Disorders
- Depression Disorders
- Bipolar Disorders
- Obsessive Compulsive Disorder (OCD)
- Post-Traumatic Stress Disorder (PTSD)
- Psychosis

GOOD TO KNOW

✓ Postpartum Depression is the #1 complication from childbirth.

✓ Up to 20% of women experience a Postpartum Mood and Anxiety Disorder.

✓ Anxiety can be just as common as depression during this time, and you can experience both at the same time.

✓ Symptoms of Postpartum Mood and Anxiety Disorders typically develop 2-3 months postpartum; however, some women experience symptoms shortly after birth and others closer to a year postpartum. Every woman is different.

✓ There are many factors that can contribute to Postpartum Mood and Anxiety Disorders including genetics, hormone shifts, sleep deprivation, level of support, trauma, environmental/financial/relationship stress.

✓ Symptoms of medical disorders, like thyroid issues, can mimic symptoms of depression and anxiety. It is recommended to check in with your primary care provider (as well as a mental health provider) for a full workup.

✓ Dads, same-sex partners, and non-biological parents can develop PMADs as well.

✓ Postpartum Mood and Anxiety Disorders are treatable. You are not alone.

POSTPARTUM MOOD AND ANXIETY DISORDERS (PMADs)

ANXIETY	OCD	PTSD	DEPRESSION	BIPOLAR	PSYCHOSIS
Constant worry Feeling that something bad is going to happen Racing thoughts Disrupted sleep and reduced appetite Inability to sit still Dizziness, hot flashes, nausea / upset stomach, claustrophobia Panic attacks	Thoughts that pop into your head regularly about harm coming to baby (also called Intrusive Thoughts) that are scary and upsetting Doing the same behavior repeatedly, usually in order to avoid "harm" A sense of horror about these thoughts These thoughts can also include thoughts of hurting yourself or even suicidal thoughts Fear of being left alone with the baby Significant worry about protecting the baby	Thoughts going over and over in your head of a traumatic event (which could be the childbirth itself) Flashbacks or nightmares Avoiding anything that reminds you of the event Irritability and difficulty sleeping Feeling like you need to be "on guard" Feeling jumpy Anxiety and panic attacks	Sad mood most of the day, nearly every day Decreased interest in pleasure Disrupted sleep and appetite Agitation, anger Fatigue or loss of energy Negative self talk Feelings of worthlessness or excessive guilt Decreased concentration Recurrent thoughts of death (self or baby) Suicidal thoughts	Shifts in mood between depression (previous column) and (Hypo)mania (Hypo)mania: Racing thoughts Having a lot of ideas at once Speaking rapidly Agitation or rage Insomnia Feeling invincible Risky behavior Heightened sex drive Impulsivity Thoughts of hurting yourself or someone else Hypomania vs. mania the intensity of symptoms Sometimes childbirth can "trigger" a bipolar disorder that was not detectable until then	Extremely rare and onset is quick. Usually support people notice significant changes in behavior over a few day period Confusion about what is real, strange beliefs (delusions) Hearing or seeing things others cannot (hallucinations) Hyperactivity Severe insomnia (no sleep for 48 hours) or not needing to sleep Very suspicious of others (Paranoia) Rapid mood swings Feeling a sense of unreality and detachment Strongly related to a bipolar disorder Hesitation to tell anyone about the symptoms

This spectrum does not provide an exhaustive list of all diagnoses and symptoms; it provides the most common ones. It is important to know some women may experience symptoms from multiple columns. Many symptoms overlap and it can be confusing to understand them all. You don't have to figure it all out. Reach out for more help when you have questions.

SEEK IMMEDIATE HELP IF: You are experiencing thoughts of wanting to hurt yourself, someone else or any symptoms listed above under 'Psychosis'. ***Call 911, or go to your nearest Emergency Room. Call the National Suicide Prevention Lifeline at 1-800-273-8255***

POSTPARTUM MOOD AND ANXIETY DISORDERS (PMADs)

YOU MAY BE AT RISK FOR PMADs IF YOU:

- Experienced mood, anxiety, and/or psychotic disorders with previous pregnancies/ postpartum periods
- Had mental health issues (anxiety, depression, etc.) before pregnancy
- Stopped your psychiatric medication when you learned you were pregnant
  Note, talk with your doctor before stopping any of your medication
- Were diagnosed or have a family member diagnosed with bipolar disorder
- Have a family history of mental illness
- Experienced trauma in childhood, adolescence, or as an adult including physical, sexual, verbal and/or emotional abuse/neglect
- Have lost a baby (miscarriage, abortion, stillbirth, infant loss)
- Experienced fertility issues (difficulty getting/staying pregnant, IVF/IUI)
- Had a difficult pregnancy and/or birth, including a traumatic birth, medical complications with either yourself or your baby
- Had a baby with a Neonatal Intensive Care Unit (NICU) stay
- Are a woman of color or any minority
- Have a baby through adoption or a surrogate mother
- Have a baby with colic
- Have twins or multiples
- Have limited support
- Had an unplanned or unwanted pregnancy
- Have a stressful relationship with your support person
- Have stressful life circumstances

IMPORTANT TO NOTE:

Just because you may have risk factor(s) does not mean you will experience a PMAD. It simply means you, your support people and your providers should have open conversations about your feelings and keep an eye on any significant changes in your mood.

POSTPARTUM MOOD AND ANXIETY DISORDERS (PMADs)

WHAT TO LOOK FOR

- Significant trouble sleeping – sleeping too much or too little (if NO sleep in 48 hours, reach out for more help)
- Significant changes in appetite – eating too much or too little, with significant weight loss/gain
- Losing interest in things you normally enjoy, and/or having no motivation
- Not wanting to take care of yourself – shower, brush your teeth, get dressed, etc.
- Feelings of being overwhelmed, sadness that doesn't go away, or hopelessness
- Uncontrolled worry
- Scary thoughts about harm coming to your baby, someone you love, or yourself
- Poor concentration and/or difficulty making every day decisions
- Increased irritability
- Severe anxiety and panic attacks
- Isolation
- Not wanting to hold or bond with your baby
- Thoughts, intent, plans to kill yourself or someone else

Note, this is not an exhaustive list.

IF YOU NOTICE ANY OF THESE SYMPTOMS FOR MORE THAT TWO WEEKS, OR IF YOU'RE SUFFERING AT ANY POINT, REACH OUT TO YOUR PROFESSIONAL SUPPORT NETWORK FOR FURTHER ASSESSMENT.

Getting help starts by letting someone know how you are really feeling. See the Maternal Mental Health Checklist on page 53 to help identify any symptoms you may be experiencing, and to help start a conversation with your support network.

* WHEN TO REACH OUT FOR MORE SUPPORT *

These are considered emergencies. Go to the nearest Emergency Department or call 911.

- Thoughts of hurting yourself
- Thoughts of hurting someone else
- Experiencing any delusions, paranoia, and/or hallucinations

Getting Help Starts by Letting Someone Know

PREPARATION AND PREVENTION

No one wants to think about being in a mental health crisis – but it is more complicated when you don't have a plan. Preparation provides direction when things can feel out of control.

---

1. WHEN DO I KNOW I NEED TO CALL MY DOCTOR? This is to be completed in collaboration with your mental health provider (therapist, psychiatrist, etc.).
Example: I haven't slept in 24 hours, I can't eat, I worry a lot. When in doubt… call!
Reference page 15 for your professional support network contacts and their info.

....

....

2. CREATE A PLAN WITH MY DOCTOR ABOUT WHAT HE/SHE WANTS ME TO WATCH FOR AROUND WORSENING MENTAL HEALTH SYMPTOMS AND WHAT TO DO.
LIST THE PLAN HERE:

....

....

....

FOR URGENT CONCERNS:

NATIONAL SUICIDE PREVENTION LIFELINE **1-800-273-8255**

3. WHERE IS THE NEAREST EMERGENCY ROOM?

....

4. HOW WILL I GET THERE? (CALL SUPPORT PERSON, CALL 911)

....

RESOURCES

There are many types of support and many ways to access support. Below is a list of professionals who can help. Become familiar with your local postpartum practitioners. And if the first person you call can't help, ask for whom they would recommend. See GLOSSARY page 73 for definition of the providers.

PRIMARY PROVIDERS

OBGYN or Midwife
Pediatrician
Primary Care Doctor

ADDITIONAL PROVIDERS

(As needed for your unique situation)

Birth, overnight and/or postpartum doula
Lactation Consultant
Therapist
Psychiatrist
Pregnancy and Postpartum Support Groups
Placenta Encapsulator
Chiropractor
Acupuncturist
Massage Therapist
Pre and Postnatal Yoga Instructor

QUESTIONS TO ASK DURING INITIAL CALL

Do you take insurance?

What is your fee?

What is your cancellation policy?

Can I bring my baby with me?

About how long will the appointment take?

Is there a private place for me to feed my baby if needed?

As applicable: Do you offer tele-medicine or tele-therapy so I can get support while at home?

What treatment options do you use in your practice?

RESOURCES

THERE ARE SUPPORT OPTIONS FOR POSTPARTUM MOOD AND ANXIETY DISORDERS AND YOUR PROVIDER CAN HELP DECIDE WHICH IS BEST FOR YOU. SOME OPTIONS INCLUDE:

SUPPORT GROUPS
A gathering of people who have common experiences and issues (in person or online). They gather to provide support, ideas and encouragement. Support groups are not considered treatment.

POSTPARTUM DOULA
In-home service provided by a professional to help with emotional and practical support (allowing mom to process/talk about her emotions, caring for the baby so the mother/family can rest, breast/bottle feeding support, newborn care, helping with household tasks).

TALK THERAPY
Proven to be an effective treatment for women with postpartum mood and anxiety disorders. Talk therapy involves meeting with a licensed, mental health professional, typically weekly to discuss how you are feeling and difficulties you are facing. Ideally your licensed mental health provider has specialized training in working with postpartum mood and anxiety disorders. Some talk therapy treatments include: Cognitive Behavioral Therapy (CBT), Interpersonal Therapy (IPT) and Eye Movement Desensitization Reprocessing (EMDR). In talk therapy, you may meet with a therapist by yourself (individual therapy), with your partner (couples counseling) or with other people facing similar struggles (group counseling). See Glossary for more details on these.

MEDICATION
May be recommended by your provider (either prescribed and/or over the counter). This is a personal decision to be made with thoughtful consideration by you and your provider. Be sure to discuss the benefits and risks of taking medication with your provider.

BEHAVIORAL HEALTH HOSPITAL BASED PROGRAMS
May be recommended for those who need more intensive treatment (can be either outpatient or inpatient programs). You or your support person should talk with the hospital staff about what to expect. If you are breastfeeding, make sure to ask how they can support you with this.

EDINBURGH POSTNATAL DEPRESSION SCALE (EPDS)
Any of the above mentioned providers may ask you to take the EPDS. This is a questionnaire used to get a better idea of how you are feeling. It will not provide you with a diagnosis, but will help your provider know how bad you are feeling and possible next steps. See Glossary for more details.

RESOURCES

POSTPARTUM SUPPORT AND PARENTING

POSTPARTUM SUPPORT INTERNATIONAL (PSI)

Support for Postpartum Mood and Anxiety Disorders. Call the PSI helpline at **1-800-944-4773** or text **503-894-9453** for local resources, support groups and providers. PSI Chat with an Expert - Free, monthly live phone sessions facilitated by a licensed mental health professional (separate sessions for mothers and partners). Resources provided in multiple languages. **postpartum.net**

POSTPARTUM STRESS CENTER

Support for women and families struggling with postpartum depression and anxiety. **postpartumstress.com**

BLACK MAMAS MATTER ALLIANCE

Serves as a national entity working to advance black maternal health, rights, and justice, and uplifts the work of locally based, black women-led maternal health initiatives and organizations. **blackmamasmatter.org**

ASIAN AMERICANS MOMS

An article offering an Asian American mom's experience with postpartum depression and anxiety in light of cultural differences. Go to **hyphenmagazine.com** and type in: "Smiling selfies and other lies" in the search feature.

LATINA MOMS

An article providing culturally sensitive thoughts on postpartum mood and anxiety disorders for Latinas. Go to **seleni.org/** and type in "Latina moms" in the search feature.

NATIONAL ALLIANCE OF MENTAL ILLNESS (NAMI)

Offers education and resources on mental illness **nami.org**

NATIONAL INSTITUTE OF MENTAL HEALTH

Leading federal agency on mental health research **nimh.nih.gov**

NEW DAD MANUAL

Information and resources created for dads, regarding parenting and self care. **newdadmanual.ca**

RESOURCES

POSTPARTUM SUPPORT AND PARENTING

GAY PARENTS TO BE

Resources for LGBTQ couples and individuals as they navigate all of the options to bring a child into the world.
gayparentstobe.com

PARENTS WITHOUT PARTNERS

Nonprofit organization devoted to the welfare and interests of single parents and their children.
parentswithoutpartners.org

NORTH AMERICAN COUNCIL ON ADOPTABLE CHILDREN

Information, resources and support groups for adoptive parents. **nacac.org**

SEX

Information regarding sex after having a baby. Go to **mayoclinic.org** and type "Set your own timeline" in the search feature.

INFANT RISK CENTER

Information regarding medications and pregnancy/breastfeeding. **Infantrisk.com**

INFANT CARE

PERIOD OF PURPLE CRYING

Educates parents around the meaning of baby's cries, and resources for soothing and self-care. **purplecrying.info**

THE NATIONAL COALITION FOR INFANT HEALTH

Educates and advocates on behalf of premature infants from birth to age two. Resources for care and treatment for babies. **infanthealth.org**

RESOURCES

BREASTFEEDING

LA LECHE LEAGUE (LLL)
Breastfeeding help, support, and local resources/support groups. **llli.org**

WOMEN INFANT AND CHILDREN (WIC) BREASTFEEDING SUPPORT
Breastfeeding support and information. **wicbreastfeeding.fns.usda.gov**

KELLY MOM
Evidence-based information on breastfeeding and parenting. **kellymom.com**

INFERTILITY

RESOLVE - THE NATIONAL INFERTILITY ASSOCIATION
Resources and support for infertility issues. **resolve.org**

CIRCLE + BLOOM
Programs to help the mind and body connection for healthy conception. **circlebloom.com**

TRAUMA

SOLACE FOR MOTHERS
Support and resources for mothers that have experienced birth trauma. **facebook.com/SolaceForMothers/**

BIRTH TRAUMA ASSOCIATION
Offers support and education to women who experienced birth trauma (based in the UK)
birthtraumaassociation.org.uk

RESOURCES

NICU

HAND TO HOLD

Helps families before, during, and after a NICU stay and infant loss by providing powerful resources for the whole family, and most importantly, one-on-one mentoring from someone who has been there. **handtohold.org**

MARCH OF DIMES

Advocating for women and babies' health. **marchofdimes.org**

BEREAVEMENT/LOSS

STILL BIRTHDAY

Support for pregnancy and infant loss. **stillbirthday.org**

COMMUNITY

HIKE IT BABY

Connects parents through getting outside in nature with their children. Search for local groups/hikes in your area. **hikeitbaby.com**

MEETUP

Connects parents and families in the postpartum period to help build community.
meetup.com/topics/postpartum

RESOURCES

BOOKS

Even June Cleaver Would Forget the Juice Box: Cut Yourself Some Slack (and Still Raise Great Kids) in the Age of Extreme Parenting by Ann L. Dunnewold, PhD

This Isn't What I Expected: Overcoming Postpartum Depression by Karen Kleiman, LCSW

Postpartum Depression for Dummies by Shoshana Bennett, PhD

The Postpartum Husband: Practical Solutions for Living with Postpartum Depression by Karen Kleiman, LCSW

The Post-Adoption Blues: Overcoming the Unforeseen Challenges of Adoption by Karen J. Foli PhD and John R. Thompson MD

Moods in Motion: A Coloring and Healing Book for Postpartum Moms by Karen Kleiman, LCSW

How to Not Hate Your Husband After Kids by Jancee Dunn

Good Moms Have Scary Thoughts: A Healing Guide to the Secret Fears of New Mothers by Karen Kleiman, LCSW

TOOLS

MINDFULNESS APPS

Guided meditations to help you manage anxiety, lower stress and sleep better.
calm.com **insighttimer.com** **headspace.com**

BABY REGISTRY

Allows parents to create a baby registry list from any store and/or service. **babylist.com**

MEALS

Friends and family can sign up to bring parents meals at home. **mealtrain.com**

BABYSITTER/NANNY

Search local providers for infant/child care services. **care.com**

YOU ARE **BRAVE.**
YOU ARE **STRONG.**
YOU ARE **EVERYTHING**
YOU NEED TO BE
RIGHT NOW.

TOOLBOX TABLE OF CONTENTS

Section 1

Section 2

Section 3

10 Things To Do Anytime You Feel Overwhelmed, Sad or Anxious

1	Step outside and get some fresh air or take a walk around the block (with baby, or by yourself), even for 5 minutes.
2	Notice where your shoulders are. Are they up towards your ears and tight? You want to send signals to your brain that you are calm and safe (relaxed shoulders), not in a place of anxiety or stress (tight shoulders).
3	Have a mantra – write it down, say it often (Example: I am strong, my body is a miracle, It's ok to feel whatever I feel, I am a good mom, I can do this).
4	Take a shower, change your clothes, get dressed in whatever makes you feel good.
5	Put on your favorite movie, watch funny videos online, anything that makes you laugh.
6	Write your thoughts down - in a journal, your computer, phone, a scratch piece of paper, record your voice.
7	Eat a healthy meal or snack and drink a big glass of water.
8	Turn on some music! Listen to your favorite tunes.
9	Move your body for a few minutes. Do arm circles, raise your calves by moving up and down on your toes, walk in place, do squats. Increasing your oxygen flow can decrease stress and burn off anxiety.
10	Ground yourself through your senses. Take a deep breath and notice 5 things around you - find one thing you can smell, hear, see, touch and taste. Keep doing this as needed.

BREATHING TECHNIQUES

Being aware of your breathing is very important, especially in times of stress. The way we breathe sends signals to our body and brain about our stress levels. Short, shallow breaths common with stress, sends signals that we need to be on alert. Breathing techniques help to remind our body and brain to remain calm. On a deeper level, deep breathing, specifically breathing through the nose, helps to produce nitric oxide, a chemical that lowers your blood pressure and has an overall calming effect.

For all the techniques below, find a quiet, peaceful place, where you can have some uninterrupted time. Some of these techniques make recommendations about sitting or laying down. Feel free to modify based on your body's needs; do what feels best for you.

Square Breathing - can be helpful to give an anxious brain something to do

- Close your eyes and exhale slowly
- Slowly take a breath in, on the count of four. *As you do this, create a square in your mind. Right now, this square only has four dots at each corner (no lines at this point).*
- Hold for the count of four. *While holding, focus on the first dot.*
- Slowly breathe out and count to four. *As you're breathing out, draw a straight line from the first dot to the second dot.*
- Repeat 3 more times until the square is complete.

Vary Your Inhalation/Exhalation - breathing out on a longer count increases sense of calm

- Take one slow, deep breath in through your nose
- Hold for the count of three
- Breathe out on the count of five through your mouth

Make sure your exhalations are longer than your inhalations.

Lioness Breathing - imagine you are a strong lioness to create sense of strength

- Close your eyes
- Take a long, deep breath, slowly filling your belly with air
- When you can't take in any more air, open your mouth as wide as you can
- Let out an "ahh" or roar sound as loud as possible while exhaling

Om breathing - the om sound is pronounced A-U-M

- Close your eyes
- Draw your breath in
- Exhale through your mouth, making an Om sound
- Try to make sure you pay equal attention to each sound - "Ooommm"
- Draw the sound from deep in your belly

DEEP BREATHING

Diaphramic Breathing - deep belly breathing

- Lie down with a pillow under your head and under your knees
- Place one hand on your upper chest, and the other just below your rib cage
- Breathe in slowly through your nose, filling your belly with air
- You should notice your hand below your rib cage is rising. Your hand on your chest should not move
- Once your belly is full of air, slowly exhale through your mouth
- Repeat at least 5 more times

Progressive Muscle Relaxation - create contrast between tightness and softness to increase a sense of relaxation

- Pick a place to start on your body - either at the top of your head or the bottom of your feet
- You will slowly move down (or up) your body, focusing on different muscle groups
- Take a deep breath
- Tighten your forehead/eyebrows so you feel tension. You want it to feel tight (but not painful) and you may even notice some shaking
- Be careful to just tighten the part you are focused on
- Hold for 5 seconds
- Breathe out and release the tension
- Notice the relaxation for about 15 seconds
- Move your attention down to your jaw and repeat the process
- Continue until you've worked your way down to your toes (or up to your head)

Affirmations and Breathing - breathe out the negative, breathing in the positive

- Notice a worried thought and think about what you prefer to believe about the situation instead (affirmation)
- Example:
  - Worried thought, "I'm never going to sleep again"
  - Pick a color for the worried thought: GRAY
  - Affirmation "this is a temporary time that ends"
  - Pick a color for the affirmation: PINK
- Close your eyes, holding your worried thought and its color in mind
- Take a breath in
- Exhale, imagine pushing out the worried thought/color out through your mouth
- Breathe in the affirmation/color as you take another breath
- Imagine the affirmation and is positive colored light filling your body
- It can be helpful to imagine the worried thought and affirmation as different colors

MATERNAL MENTAL HEALTH CHECKLIST

This is a tool that can be used to help identify postpartum emotions and symptoms of postpartum mood and anxiety disorders (PMADS). While some PMADs are common after having a baby, they can often be difficult to talk about. This tool can help generate conversations with the appropriate people to provide mothers with support and treatment as needed. **Mothers, you are not alone! There is always help, and PMADs can be treated.**

Mom's Name: ______________________ **Mom's Age:** _______ **Total # of children living at home:** ________

Directions: Please read and check all the appropriate boxes to describe how you are feeling, and share this checklist with your partner/spouse/support person/OBGyn/primary doctor.

>> I'd like to talk to you about the stress that I've been having since I had my baby. Because I am exhausted, overwhelmed and struggling, this is the best way for me to make sure you know what is going on with me, and that I might need your help. I think that I may have (Mom, check any that may apply):

- ☐ Postpartum depression (PPD)
- ☐ Postpartum anxiety or OCD
- ☐ Postpartum post-traumatic stress disorder (PTSD)
- ☐ Postpartum psychosis
- ☐ Bipolar disorder or mania
- ☐ Not sure, I just know something isn't right

Here are some of the recognized symptoms of PMADs that I have been experiencing (Mom, check any that apply to you):

- ☐ I can't sleep, even when my baby is sleeping.
- ☐ I feel sad. I have been crying a lot for no reason.
- ☐ I have lost my appetite.
- ☐ I am feeling anxious or worried most of the time.
- ☐ I am having rage/anger that is not typical of me.
- ☐ I feel numb or disconnected from my life. I can't enjoy the things I used to.
- ☐ I do not feel like I am bonding with my baby.
- ☐ I am having scary "what if" intrusive thoughts over and over about harm coming to me, or my baby.
- ☐ I feel a lot of guilt and shame.
- ☐ I am worried that I am not a good mother.
- ☐ I feel overwhelmed with all of the things in my life.
- ☐ I cannot concentrate or stay focused on things.
- ☐ I feel like I'm losing it.
- ☐ I want to be alone most of the time.
- ☐ My thoughts are racing. I cannot sit still.
- ☐ I feel like the only way to feel better is by using alcohol, prescription drugs, or other substances.
- ☐ Sometimes I wonder if my baby or family would be better off without me.
- ☐ I have been experiencing physical symptoms that are not typical for me (for example, migraines, back/stomach aches, shortness of breath, panic attacks).
- ☐ I have serious thoughts of hurting myself.
- ☐ I have thoughts that I should (not that I might, or what if, but that I should or need to) hurt my baby or someone else.
- ☐ I am worried that I am seeing or hearing things that other people don't see or hear.
- ☐ I am afraid to be alone with my baby.
- ☐ I feel very concerned or paranoid that other people may hurt me.

I have experienced these symptoms for more than _____ weeks. I am ______ weeks/months (circle one) postpartum.

This can be cut out and shared with your provider.

MATERNAL MENTAL HEALTH CHECKLIST

Here are some recognized risk factors for maternal mental health issues that may help you understand my situation
(Mom, check any that apply to you):

- ☐ I have experienced depression, anxiety, OCD or PPD before.
- ☐ I have a history of bipolar disorder or psychosis.
- ☐ My family has a history of mental illness.
- ☐ I have a history of trauma, or I am going through trauma (for example, domestic/verbal/physical/sexual abuse, poverty, grief/loss).
- ☐ I have had a stressful event in the last year (for example, moving, job loss/change, divorce/relationship problems, grief/loss).
- ☐ I am a single mom.
- ☐ I don't have help or support at home from my partner or family.
- ☐ I have a lot of financial stress.
- ☐ I had infertility treatment.
- ☐ My baby has colic, reflux or other health problems.
- ☐ I experienced a previous miscarriage or stillbirth.
- ☐ I have a medical history of diabetes, thyroid problems, or menstrual issues.
- ☐ I am away from my home country or culture.
- ☐ I delivered multiples.
- ☐ I or my baby had problems in pregnancy or childbirth (for example, baby in NICU, unplanned c-section, bed rest)
- ☐ Any additional thoughts or concerns that are on your mind: ____________________

____

____

____

____

____

____

____

____

____

____

____

____

This checklist is not intended to diagnose any mental disorder. It is a discussion tool for moms to use with healthcare providers.

This can be cut out and shared with your provider.

TOOLBOX

DO | DELEGATE | DUMP

After having a baby, it is important to focus on what is absolutely necessary to get done on a daily basis to conserve your time, energy and head space. Create a list to identify what needs to be done, what can be delegated, and what can wait until a later time.

DO

WHAT YOU ABSOLUTELY NEED TO DO.
Example: Feed the baby, personal hygiene, care for C-section scar or vaginal tear

DELEGATE

WHAT NEEDS TO GET DONE BUT ANOTHER CAN DO.
Example: Walk the dog, make a meal, any calls about follow up appointments or to the insurance company

DUMP

WHAT YOU HOPE TO GET DONE BUT CAN WAIT.
Example: Clean the house, do the laundry

MAKE A DONE LIST

List out all the things you've done today (vs. a to-do list which can be daunting and not doable). REMEMBER: what you're able to get done may look different than what you were able to do before — be kind to yourself! Example: Fed my baby, changed four poop diapers, took a shower, etc.

NEED HELP ASKING FOR HELP?

GIVE THIS A TRY...

"Thank you so much for your love and support during this time. Today I need help with ________"

EITHER ASK VERBALLY OR WRITE AS A NOTE TO POST ON YOUR FRIDGE OR ANOTHER VISIBLE PLACE.

JOURNALING

Journaling can be a helpful way to understand and express your emotions during the postpartum time. It can also help release fears, worries, and anxious thoughts when you are not able to explain these feelings with spoken words. There is no right or wrong way to journal. Simply write what is on your mind either on the following pages or in a different journal. Do not worry about spelling or punctuation. Let your thoughts flow naturally! Here are some prompts to get you started:

Today I am grateful for... I feel at ease when... I am so proud of myself for... What made me feel good during a difficult experience in the past? How did I overcome it?

AFFIRMATIONS

Affirmations are a wonderful way to help overcome fear, boost confidence, and develop a mindset of positivity. Affirmations are simple positive statements or declarations.

They are used to challenge negative self talk. It's ok to not fully believe an affirmation at first, but if there's a part of you that wants to believe it, start there. Practicing using affirmations makes them more believable.

YOU CAN USE AFFIRMATIONS IN DIFFERENT WAYS:

- Pick a few you like and post them around your home
- Pick one each morning to set a mindset of positivity throughout the day
- Share the ones that resonate with you with friends
- Come up with an entirely different way to use them that's all your own!

Cut on the dotted lines to remove the cards.

I love MYSELF NO MATTER WHAT

I'M NOT THE PERFECT MOTHER, BUT I'M **EXACTLY THE ONE MY CHILDREN NEED.**

PEACE COMES WHEN I LET GO OF TRYING TO CONTROL EVERY TINY DETAIL.

I face difficult situations with COURAGE & CONVICTION

THERE'S VALUE
IN SHOWING MY KIDS
MY VULNERABILITY.

TODAY I WILL
see the best in my baby, and
the best in myself.

I SPEAK
KINDLY
TO MYSELF.

I'm proud of myself
for attempting
new things.

**I release myself
from carrying the
burdens of my past.**

Being a good mom means
I nurture myself and
take care of my needs also.

I BELIEVE
IN MYSELF
as a capable and
wonderful mother.

***Today I give myself
permission to be greater
than my fears.***

MAKE YOUR OWN AFFIRMATIONS

I am…

Today is better because…

Everyday I realize that…

SELF CARE REMINDER CARDS

Below is a list of prompt/reminder cards you can place around your home to help check in with how you are doing. There are several blank cards that you can personalize based on your individual needs. Remember to pause for a second before reading these cards. Pausing will help you turn your focus to the prompts, allowing you to more easily check in with yourself.

AM I
THIRSTY?

DO I NEED TO
GO TO THE
BATHROOM?

DO I NEED TO
USE A BREATHING
TECHNIQUE?

DO I NEED TO
CALL A
SUPPORT
PERSON?

AM I
HUNGRY?

WHAT IS A TOOL
FROM MY TOOLBOX,
I CAN USE RIGHT NOW?

Am I…

Am I…

Am I…

Am I…

Do I…

Do I…

What is…

What is…

Am I...

Am I...

Am I...

Am I...

Do I...

Do I...

What is...

What is...

GLOSSARY

The following are definitions of terms as they are used within this workbook.

ACUPUNCTURIST - A provider trained in Traditional Chinese Medicine who works to help relieve pain and promote healing. An acupuncturist can treat imbalances in the body (such as stress, insomnia, or anxiety) that may occur in the postpartum period.

AFFIRMATION - A statement about oneself or about one's skills or strength that is declared to be true to promote self-empowerment and positive thinking. Affirmations can be written, spoken out loud, or read on a daily basis to help a person through any period of transition.

ANXIETY - The body's response to stress that can cause feelings like fear or worry, racing thoughts, and bodily sensations such as increased heart rate, tight shoulders, and upset stomach. Anxiety is a treatable condition.

BABY BLUES - Common feelings of sadness and irritability and symptoms such as crying in mothers that typically appear 4-5 days after delivering a baby. Baby blues are not considered a mental health issue, and typically resolve, on their own, within a few weeks after delivery.

BEHAVIORAL HEALTH HOSPITAL - A hospital that specializes in providing mental health care services ranging from inpatient hospitalization, for psychiatric emergencies (spending the night(s) in the hospital), to outpatient services (going to the hospital during the day for treatment and home at night).

BIPOLAR DISORDER - A mental health condition that causes unusual, at times extreme, shifts in moods and energy levels. Includes alternating between depression and (hypo)mania. Bipolar is a treatable condition.

BIRTH DOULA - A professional trained in childbirth who provides emotional, physical, and educational support to a mother (and support person) during pregnancy, labor, and delivery. A birth doula's purpose is to help women have a safe, memorable, and empowering birthing experience.

CHIROPRACTOR - A medical provider focused on the proper alignment of the spine to relieve tension and pain during pregnancy and the postpartum period. A chiropractor can use techniques to help flip a breech baby during pregnancy.

COGNITIVE BEHAVIORAL THERAPY (CBT) - An evidenced based, talk therapy treatment for many mental health disorders. CBT is one of the leading treatments used for postpartum depression and anxiety. In CBT, a client learns about the connection between her unhelpful/dysfunctional thoughts, feelings and behaviors, and how making a change in one of these areas creates change in the others.

GLOSSARY

COLIC - Periods of intense, loud, and inconsolable crying in an infant. The crying occurs with no defined reason for 3 or more hours a day, 3 or more days of the week, and for more than 3 weeks in a row. It is common in infants, and any concerns should be addressed with the baby's pediatrician.

DEPRESSION - A mental health condition characterized by a consistent sad or depressed mood, feelings of hopelessness, and loss of interest in activities. Symptoms make it hard to complete daily activities like sleeping, eating, and working. Depression is a treatable condition.

EDINBURGH POSTNATAL DEPRESSION SCALE (EPDS) - The standard screening scale used by providers to assess for postpartum depression. It includes 10 questions that help identify symptoms of depression and issues with sleep disturbance, low energy, and suicidal ideation. It cannot diagnose women with depression, but it helps the provider know if further investigation is needed to determine a diagnosis.

EMOTIONAL HEALTH - The focus on emotional and mental well-being, including the awareness and management of thoughts, feelings, and behaviors. The equal counterpart to physical health.

EYE MOVEMENT DESENSITIZATION REPROCESSING (EMDR) - A type of therapy that treats many mental health disorders, including trauma. An EMDR trained, licensed mental health provider will ask the client to follow his/her fingers back and forth (with just the client's eyes) while the client recalls details of a stressful event. This back and forth movement of the eyes is thought to replicate what is happening in REM sleep. It is believed that during REM sleep, memories are stored and moods are balanced. EMDR can be used to treat birth traumas.

GRIEF AND LOSS - The feelings of sadness, despair, and emptiness that arise after a loss occurs. It can be a loss from any experience and varies greatly from person to person. Mothers often feel grief after a miscarriage/perinatal loss and during shifts in identity, employment, and social interactions during the postpartum period.

HYPOMANIA - Symptoms include impulsivity, poor sleep, racing thoughts, agitation/rage, having a lot of energy, talking fast and a feeling of being "on top of the world," and dangerous/reckless behavior. Someone diagnosed with bipolar disorder, type II, has hypomania and depression and fluctuates between the two. The difference between hypomania and mania is the severity of the symptoms.

IN VITRO FERTILIZATION (IVF) - A process that uses medication and medical procedures to assist sperm in fertilizing the egg outside of the woman's body. The fertilized egg is later implanted in the woman's uterus. It is a form of fertility treatment.

INTERPERSONAL THERAPY (IPT) - Focuses on the mother's relationships and ability to function, especially in social situations. IPT is an attachment based therapy that focuses on reducing a mother's symptoms. It is a time limited and evidenced based treatment. IPT is one of the leading treatments used for postpartum depression and anxiety.

GLOSSARY

INTRAUTERINE INSEMINATION (IUI) - A medical procedure in which sperm is placed inside a woman's uterus, close to the fallopian tube to increase chances of conceiving. IUI is a form of fertility treatment.

INTRUSIVE (SCARY) THOUGHTS - Upsetting thoughts mothers may have during the postpartum period that include images or frightening ideas that often focus on the baby, a loved one, or the mother herself being harmed. These thoughts are common in mothers and can be very alarming and unsettling. They often are surrounded by feelings of shame and fear. For some moms, they subside over time and other moms require talk therapy and/or medication for relief.

LACTATION CONSULTANT (LC) - A professional trained to help mothers and babies breastfeed with ease. Most hospitals have LCs on staff that you can request to see after delivery. LCs in private practice can be found in the community as well and can assist mothers within a clinic or in the mother's home.

MANIA - Symptoms include impulsivity, poor sleep, racing thoughts, agitation/rage, having a lot of energy, talking fast and a feeling of being "on top of the world," and dangerous/reckless behavior. Someone diagnosed with bipolar disorder, type I, has mania and depression and fluctuates between the two. In mania, the symptoms are more severe, even life threatening, than in hypomania. Symptoms can also include psychosis.

MENTAL HEALTH COUNSELING - see Talk Therapy

MENTAL HEALTH DISORDER - Conditions that affect thinking, feeling, mood, and behavior. They may be situational (occasional) or long-lasting (chronic). They can be caused by both genetic and environmental factors. The postpartum period is a time full of hormonal shifts which can cause mental health-like symptoms. Mental health disorders are treatable.

MIDWIFE - A provider trained and certified by the Accreditation Commission for Midwifery Education (ACME) to deliver babies and care for women both during pregnancy and after delivery. Midwives deliver babies at birth centers, at home, and in some hospitals.

NEONATAL INTENSIVE CARE UNIT (NICU) - An intensive care unit in a hospital specializing in the care of ill or premature newborn infants. Neonatal refers to the first 28 days of life.

NERVOUS SYSTEM - Helps send messages from the brain to different parts of the body. The nervous system is responsible for picking up on environmental changes that can impact the body.

OBSESSIVE COMPULSIVE DISORDER (OCD) - A mental health condition characterized by thoughts and fears (obsessions) that lead to repetitive behaviors (compulsions) that relieve the obsessions temporarily, but become reinforcing. Symptoms usually begin gradually and vary throughout the postpartum period. OCD is a treatable condition.

GLOSSARY

OBSTETRICIAN AND GYNECOLOGIST (OBGYN) - A medical provider/doctor who has attended medical school, passed state boards, and is licensed. An OBGYN specializes in caring for women. Obstetricians deliver babies and care for women during pregnancy and after delivery. A Gynecologist focuses on reproductive health and cares for women when they are not pregnant.

OVERNIGHT SLEEP DOULA - A professionally trained doula who cares for an infant during typical sleep hours so the mother/support person can sleep better.

PANIC ATTACK - A sudden feeling of intense anxiety and/or fear that causes a physical reaction such as increased heart rate, sweating, rapid pulse, shortness of breath, shaking, choking, or feeling faint. A panic attack can be very frightening and can mimic the feeling of having a heart attack. Panic attacks are treatable.

PEDIATRICIAN - A medical provider/doctor who has attended medical school, passed state boards, and is licensed. A pediatrician specializes in caring for babies, children, and adolescents. Pediatricians see babies for routine well child visits and when babies are sick.

PERINATAL - The time frame from pregnancy to one year postpartum.

PLACENTA - A large organ that develops during pregnancy that is attached to the wall of the uterus. The umbilical cord connects the placenta to the baby. Blood from the mother passes through the placenta, filtering oxygen, glucose and nutrients to the baby, and also removes waste from the baby via the umbilical cord. The placenta produces a number of hormones that are needed during pregnancy, such as estrogen and progesterone.

PLACENTA ENCAPSULATION - The process after childbirth when a certified professional steams, dehydrates, and grinds the placenta into a fine powder that is placed into capsules for consumption by the mother. Ingesting placenta can help balance a mother's hormone levels after giving birth.

PRENATAL AND POSTPARTUM YOGA - A gentle yoga practice that is tailored specifically to support the pregnant/postpartum body.

POSTPARTUM - The period from birth through 12 months. However, the postpartum period can extend past one year, especially if the mother is still breastfeeding or experiencing any symptoms of a Postpartum Mood and/or Anxiety Disorder.

POSTPARTUM DOULA - A professional trained to help mothers and families in their home and provide emotional and practical support during the postpartum period. A postpartum doula's purpose is to allow the mother/family to rest, recover and build confidence with breast/bottle feeding, newborn care, self care, nutrition, household tasks, and emotional changes.

POSTPARTUM MOOD AND ANXIETY DISORDER (PMAD) - Includes a spectrum of disorders that can occur during the postpartum period, including anxiety, depression, OCD, PTSD, and psychosis.

GLOSSARY

POSTPARTUM PLAN - A prepared written plan that includes preferences and guidelines to help support a mother and her support person during the postpartum period. It includes a focus on nutrition, sleep, support,self care, and anything else needed to educate, prepare, and empower a family.

POST-TRAUMATIC STRESS DISORDER (PTSD) - A mental health condition in which a person is exposed to a traumatic event, either directly or by witnessing one. PTSD can cause nightmares, irritability, isolation, avoidance of people or places related to the event, anxiety, insomnia, and unsettling flashbacks of the event. Two people can experience the same trauma but have different outcomes; whether or not someone develops symptoms of PTSD is highly individualized. PTSD is a treatable condition.

PRIMARY CARE PHYSICIAN (PCP) - A medical provider/doctor who has attended medical school, passed state boards, and is licensed. PCPs provide general medical care.

PROVIDER - A generic term used to describe the professionals that provide emotional and/or medical services.

PSYCHIATRIST - A medical provider/doctor who has attended medical school, passed state boards, and is licensed. A psychiatrist specializes in treating mental health disorders. Psychiatrists are able to prescribe medication. Some psychiatrists provide talk therapy as well.

PSYCHOSIS - A mental health condition in which someone experiences an altered reality. Psychosis is not a diagnosis itself but a symptom. Some of the characteristics of psychosis include hallucinations (hearing or seeing things others cannot) and delusions (paranoia or strong beliefs that seem irrational to others). Psychosis is considered an emergency that requires immediate action, however it is also treatable.

SELF CARE - The intentional care for yourself. Self care is anything that makes you feel more centered and calm. Self care works best when practiced daily and is just as important as sleeping and eating.

SUPPORT GROUPS - Peer/facilitator led groups that offer support to those going through similar experiences. It can be a good place to get tips, build community, and normalize what you may be going through. Support groups are likely not enough support for someone struggling with mental health symptoms where treatment may be necessary.

SUPPORT PERSON - A trusted, reliable person in the mother's life such as a husband, wife, boy/girl friend, partner, other family member, close friend, etc.

GLOSSARY

TALK THERAPY - Another term for mental health counseling. Talk therapy is typically a 50-60 minute session. Providers who use talk therapy as treatment are called therapists. Providers can include: psychologists (PhD or PsyD), licensed clinical social workers (LCSW), licensed professional counselors (LPC), licensed marriage and family counselor (LMFT), and psychiatrists (MD or DO). Psychiatrists are the only providers out of this list who can prescribe medication for mental health conditions. These providers use different theories to practice therapy and may see clients individually or in marriage/family sessions. Providers can specialize in treating postpartum mood and anxiety disorders.

THERAPIST - A licensed mental health provider who treats mental health concerns by providing emotional support, education on coping with challenges, and alleviating symptoms.

TRANSITION - The change from one way of being to another. In motherhood, transition is used to discuss any shift during pregnancy and throughout the postpartum period. Transition is also used to describe some of the feelings and thoughts that can come up with shifts in a mother's identity, leaving/returning to work, adjusting relationships with other children, functioning on little sleep, and changes seen within the baby.

TRAUMA - A deeply upsetting or disturbing event(s) that can affect a person emotionally and/or physically. These events could occur at any point in the mother's life including childhood, adolescence, pregnancy, birth, and/or the postpartum period. Trauma is defined by what the mother believes about the event, not by the perception of others. Women can enter the postpartum period with a history of trauma (prior to pregnancy) which can resurface during this time. Trauma is treatable.

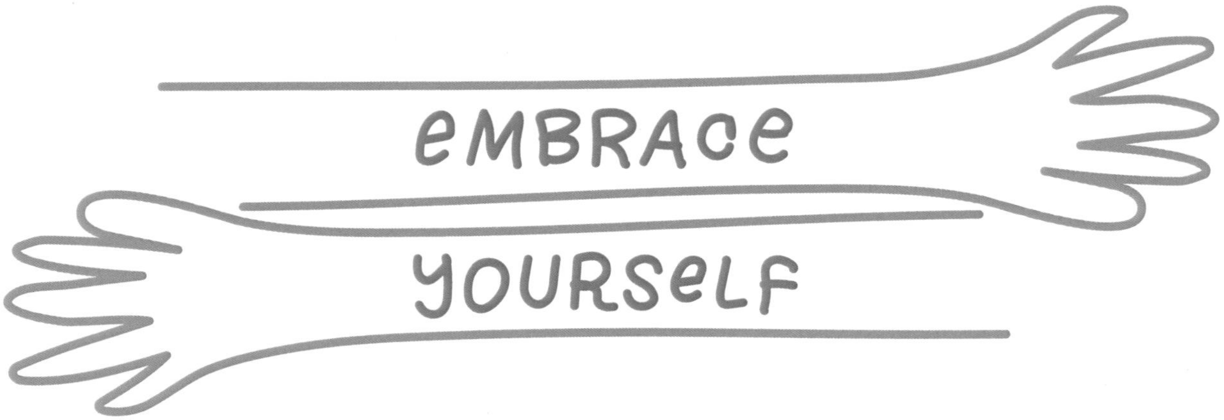

A Note from the Authors

Remember, whatever you experience during your postpartum period is unique to you. Be careful not to judge yourself against other moms, or even other pregnancies or babies you had in the past. Your current experience is valid, and every single emotion is important.

Having a baby literally changes your body and mind unlike any other experience. This is a time to honor yourself, and allow an abundance of grace and compassion into your heart and mind. Every single person must learn how to become a parent and adapt to a new way of life with a baby. This is not automatic! During this learning process, you will have the expected ups and downs of so many varying emotions. One cannot exist without the other, and healing is not linear. Please remember, there is not one solution that fits everyone. You know yourself the best, and if you feel more negative emotions than positive emotions, reach out for help. There is no need to suffer on any level.

This workbook is developed with an emphasis on emotional health and wellness, but remember your body too. Be gentle, move slow. Your body and mind are connected and are on the same team. Focus on the entire you.

And lastly, always remember, you are important and so loved.

— Authors, Amy Tucker, Postpartum Doula and Erin Fassnacht, LCSW

This workbook was created by parents, for parents.

It's rooted in a combination of both personal and professional challenges and triumphs that have been experienced firsthand as parents. Every aspect of this workbook from the content, design, editing, and everything in between was created with love by parents to support your journey.

ABOUT THE AUTHORS

AMY TUCKER // POSTPARTUM DOULA

Amy Tucker is an advocate for creating and maintaining a healthy postpartum recovery. After working in high tech industries for 12 years, it was the experience of having two children and overcoming severe postpartum depression and anxiety that ignited her passion for helping families through the postpartum transition. Amy is a DONA Postpartum Doula, Maternal Mental Health Specialist, and Owner of Mama Peace. Learn more about Amy Tucker at mamapeace.com.

ERIN FASSNACHT, LCSW // THERAPIST

Erin Fassnacht is a licensed clinical social worker with over 17 years of experience working with clients with mental health issues. She experienced her own struggles with anxiety after the birth of her two children and became invested in helping other moms to understand their experiences. Erin specializes in treating women with perinatal mood and anxiety disorders and their families. She is a strong advocate for providing education around PMADs to clients and healthcare professionals alike. Learn more about Erin Fassnacht at erinfassnacht.com.

A Note of Gratitude - We would like to express our tremendous gratitude to our partners, family and friends for all the late night support, important thoughts and conversations, and for the unending encouragement to keep on going during our own personal and professional challenges. We also want to acknowledge our amazing colleagues for their thoughtful feedback and contributions during the development and implementation of this workbook. We feel honored to help serve your clients and work by your side. And last, but certainly not least, we want to give a heart filled thank you to ALL the parents that were so brave to ask for support and share their struggles and triumphs with us over the years. You are the soul of our work.